# Theory Paper    Grade 3    2017    A

*Duration 1½ hours*

**TOTAL MARKS**
100

Candidates should answer ALL questions.
Write your answers on this paper – no others will be accepted.
Answers must be written clearly and neatly – otherwise marks may be lost.

**1**   Add the missing bar-lines to each of these **three** melodies, which all begin on the first
beat of the bar.

10

**2**   Answer **both** (a) and (b).

10

(a)   Rewrite the following melody with the notes correctly grouped (beamed).

(b)   How many demisemiquavers (32nd notes) is the first note of bar 3 (marked ↓) worth?   ............

**3** Name the key of each of the following scales. Where the key is minor, state whether the scale is in the harmonic or melodic form.

10

Key ........................................

Key ........................................

Key ........................................

Key ........................................

**4** Add the correct clef and any necessary accidentals to each of these tonic triads. Do **not** use key signatures.

10

C minor

Bb major

E major

A minor

A major

**5** **After** each of these notes write a **higher** note to form the named **melodic** interval. The key is F# minor.

10

minor 6th

major 7th

perfect 4th

perfect 8ve

major 2nd

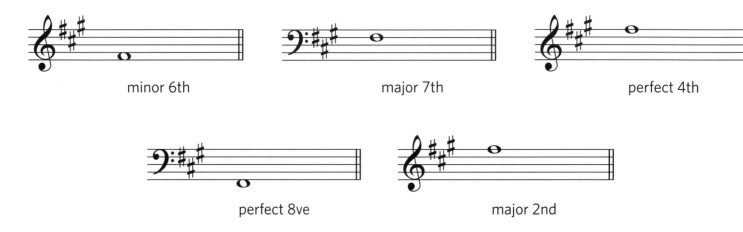

4

**6** Give the letter name of each of these notes. The first answer is given.

C sharp

..................................

..................................

..................................

..................................

..................................

**7** Rewrite this melody using notes of **twice the value**. Remember to put in the new time signature at the place marked *, and remember to group (beam) the notes correctly.

J. S. Bach

**8** Tick one box for each term, as shown in the first answer.

| *prima volta* means | | **Presto** means: | | *ritmico* means: | |
|---|---|---|---|---|---|
| first time | ✔ | slow | ☐ | held back | ☐ |
| in time | ☐ | fast | ☐ | agitated | ☐ |
| speed, time | ☐ | at a medium speed | ☐ | rhythmically | ☐ |
| second time | ☐ | broadening | ☐ | at choice | ☐ |

| **non troppo** means: | | *semplice* means: | | *rubato* means: | |
|---|---|---|---|---|---|
| very much | ☐ | suddenly | ☐ | at a comfortable speed | ☐ |
| too much | ☐ | simple, plain | ☐ | with determination | ☐ |
| not too much | ☐ | in the same way | ☐ | becoming more lively | ☐ |
| not in time | ☐ | sustained | ☐ | with some freedom of time | ☐ |

**9** Look at this melody by Haydn and then answer the questions below.

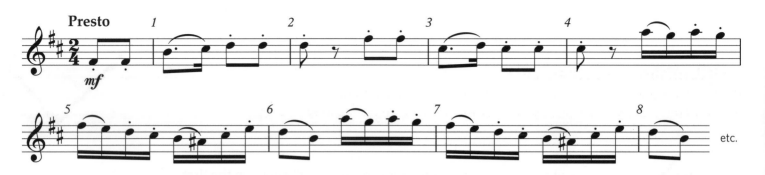

*Write your answer to question (b) on the stave below.*

(a) (i) The melody is in the key of B minor. Name the degree of the scale (e.g. 2nd, 3rd) of the first note of the melody. ............ [10]

(ii) Which other key has the same key signature as B minor? ..............................................................

(iii) Answer TRUE or FALSE to this statement:

Every complete bar in this melody contains at least one note of the tonic triad of B minor. ..........................

(iv) Complete this statement:

Bar 5 has the same notes and rhythm as bar ............. .

(v) Give the time name (e.g. crotchet or quarter note) of the **longest** note in the melody. ..................................................

(b) Using the blank stave above question (a), write out the melody from the beginning of the music to the first note of bar 4 **an octave lower**, using the bass clef as shown. [10]

# Theory Paper    Grade 3    2017   B

*Duration 1½ hours*

TOTAL MARKS
100

**Candidates should answer ALL questions.**
**Write your answers on this paper – no others will be accepted.**
**Answers must be written clearly and neatly – otherwise marks may be lost.**

1  Add the missing bar-lines to each of these **three** melodies, which all begin on the first beat of the bar.

10

'Song for Jo' from *Jazz Sessions*
© 2005 Faber Music Ltd
Extract reproduced by permission of Faber Music Ltd. All rights reserved.

2  Answer **both** (a) and (b).

10

(a)  Rewrite the following melody with the notes correctly grouped (beamed).

(b)  Describe the time signature as:  simple or compound          ..........................................

duple, triple or quadruple          ..........................................

**3** Add the correct clef and any necessary accidentals to make each of the scales named below. Do **not** use key signatures.

E major

G **harmonic** minor

**4** Describe each of these melodic intervals, giving the type and number (e.g. minor 3rd, perfect 4th). The keys are named, and in each case the lower note is the key note.

Bb major

Type ...............................

Number ...............................

F minor

Type ...............................

Number ...............................

A major

Type ...............................

Number ...............................

F# minor

Type ...............................

Number ...............................

Eb major

Type ...............................

Number ...............................

**5** Add the correct rest(s) at the places marked * in these two melodies to make each bar complete.

Valerie Capers

J. S. Bach

**6** Add the correct clef and key signature to each of these tonic triads.

10

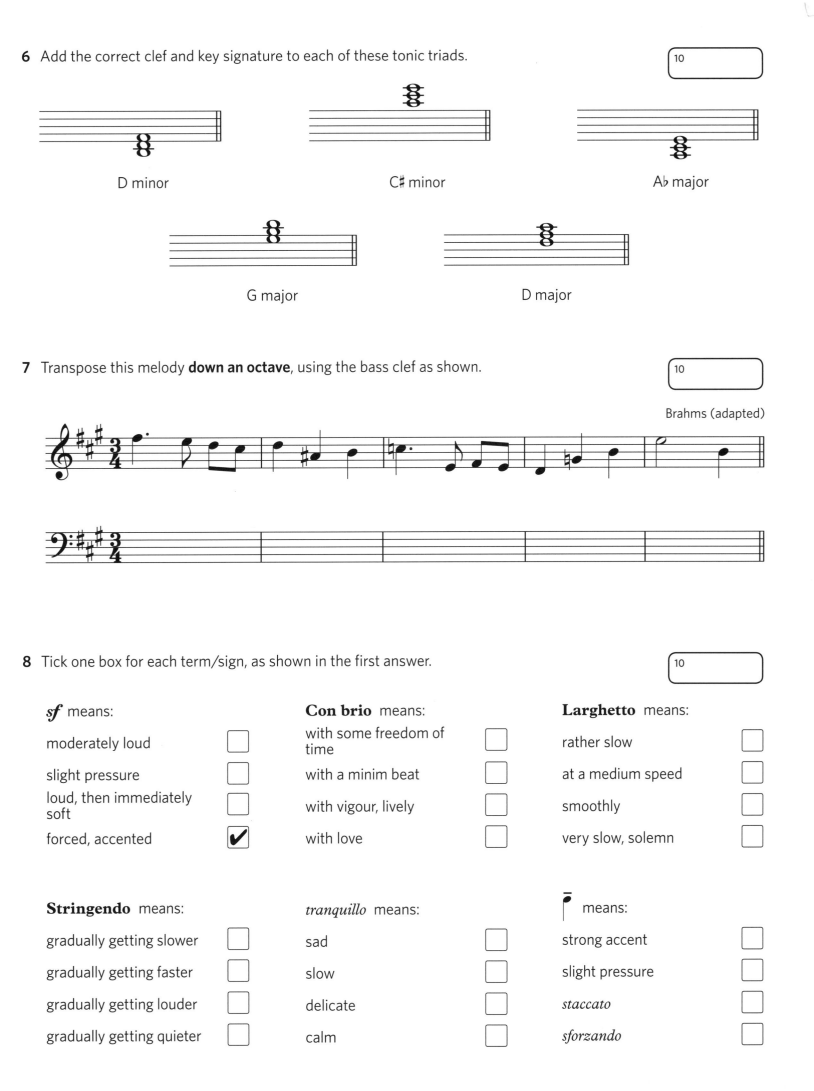

D minor

C# minor

Ab major

G major

D major

**7** Transpose this melody **down an octave**, using the bass clef as shown.

10

Brahms (adapted)

**8** Tick one box for each term/sign, as shown in the first answer.

10

| *sf* means: | |
|---|---|
| moderately loud | ☐ |
| slight pressure | ☐ |
| loud, then immediately soft | ☐ |
| forced, accented | ✔ |

| **Con brio** means: | |
|---|---|
| with some freedom of time | ☐ |
| with a minim beat | ☐ |
| with vigour, lively | ☐ |
| with love | ☐ |

| **Larghetto** means: | |
|---|---|
| rather slow | ☐ |
| at a medium speed | ☐ |
| smoothly | ☐ |
| very slow, solemn | ☐ |

| **Stringendo** means: | |
|---|---|
| gradually getting slower | ☐ |
| gradually getting faster | ☐ |
| gradually getting louder | ☐ |
| gradually getting quieter | ☐ |

| *tranquillo* means: | |
|---|---|
| sad | ☐ |
| slow | ☐ |
| delicate | ☐ |
| calm | ☐ |

| ̄𝆺 means: | |
|---|---|
| strong accent | ☐ |
| slight pressure | ☐ |
| *staccato* | ☐ |
| *sforzando* | ☐ |

**9** Look at this melody by Beethoven and then answer the questions below.

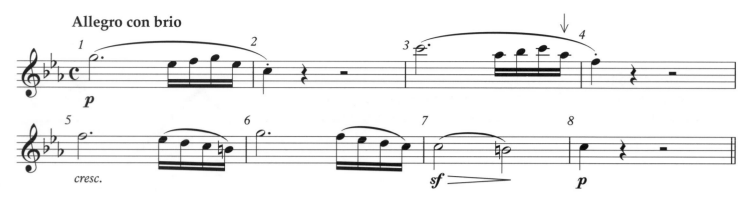

*Write your answer to question (b) on the stave below.*

(a) (i) How many demisemiquavers
(32nd notes) is the first note of the melody worth? ............

(ii) The melody is in the key of C minor. Give the number of
a bar that contains **all** the notes of the tonic triad in this key.    Bar ............

(iii) Name the degree of the scale (e.g. 2nd, 3rd) of the
last note of bar 3 (marked ↓). Remember that the key is C minor. ............

(iv) Give the letter name of the **highest** note in the melody. ............

(v) Answer TRUE or FALSE to this statement:

𝄴 and ⁴⁄₄ both mean four crotchet (quarter-note) beats in a bar. .........................

(b) Using the blank stave above question (a), write out the melody from the beginning
of bar 5 to the end of the music using notes and rests of **twice the value**. Remember to
put in the new time signature at the place marked ∗, and remember to group (beam)
the notes correctly.

# Theory Paper   Grade 3   2017   C

*Duration 1½ hours*

TOTAL MARKS
100

**Candidates should answer ALL questions.**
**Write your answers on this paper – no others will be accepted.**
**Answers must be written clearly and neatly – otherwise marks may be lost.**

**1**   Add the time signature to each of these five examples.

10

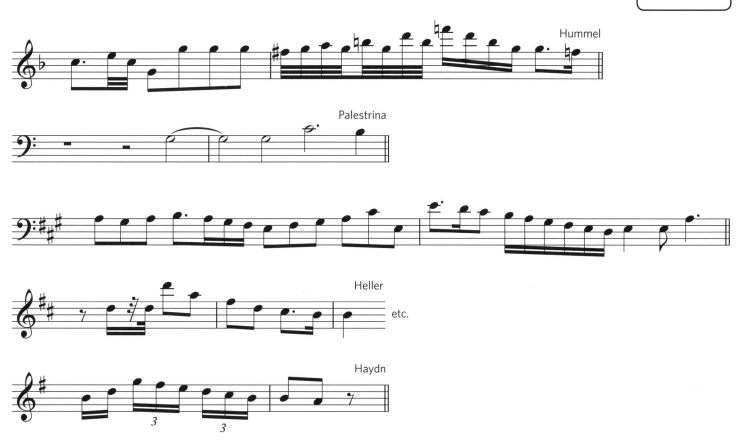

**2**   Add the correct rest(s) at the places marked * in these two melodies to make each bar complete.

10

'Groovy Movie' from *Easy Little Peppers*
© 2004 Faber Music Ltd
Extract reproduced by permission of Faber Music Ltd. All rights reserved.

**3** Describe each of these harmonic intervals, giving the type and number (e.g. major 3rd, perfect 5th). The keys are named, and in each case the lower note is the key note.

Ab major

Type ...........................

Number ...........................

B minor

Type ...........................

Number ...........................

F major

Type ...........................

Number ...........................

F minor

Type ...........................

Number ...........................

C minor

Type ...........................

Number ...........................

**4** Rewrite this melody using notes and rests of **half the value**. Remember to put in the new time signature at the place marked ∗, and remember to group (beam) the notes correctly.

Bull (adapted)

**5** Name the key of each of these tonic triads.

...........................................

...........................................

...........................................

...........................................

...........................................

**6** Give the letter name of each of these notes. The first answer is given.

10

F sharp
.................................

.................................

.................................

.................................

.................................

.................................

**7** Tick one box for each term/sign, as shown in the first answer.

10

$\lemma. = 60$ means:

60 dotted-crotchet beats in a minute ✔

60 dotted-crotchet beats ☐

60 dotted crotchets in the melody ☐

60 dotted-crotchet notes ☐

**Allegro assai** means:

fairly quick ☐

quick ☐

very quick ☐

gradually getting quicker ☐

**più mosso** means:

with movement ☐

more movement ☐

less movement ☐

without movement ☐

*amoroso* means:

agitated ☐

sad, sorrowful ☐

delicate ☐

loving ☐

*risoluto* means:

bold, strong ☐

rhythmically ☐

simple, plain ☐

becoming more lively ☐

*scherzando* means:

sweet ☐

simple, plain ☐

playful, joking ☐

forced, accented ☐

**8** Using semibreves (whole notes), write one octave of the scales named below.

F♯ **melodic** minor, **descending**, without key signature but including any necessary accidentals.

B♭ major, **ascending**, with key signature.

**9** Look at this melody, which is adapted from a piece by Wilm, and then answer the questions below.

*Write your answer to question (b) on the stave below.*

(a) (i) The melody is in the key of C major.
Which other key has the same key signature? ...................................

   (ii) The first phrase has been marked with a bracket (  ).
Mark all the other phrases in the same way.

   (iii) How many times does the rhythm  occur in this melody? ............

   (iv) Give the time name (e.g. crotchet or
quarter note) of the **longest** note in the melody. ....................................

   (v) Describe the time signature as: simple or compound ....................................

                         duple, triple or quadruple ....................................

(b) Using the blank stave above question (a), write out the melody from the beginning of
bar 1 to the end of bar 4 **an octave higher**, using the treble clef as shown.

# Theory Paper    Grade 3    2017   S

*Duration 1½ hours*

TOTAL MARKS
100

**Candidates should answer ALL questions.**
**Write your answers on this paper – no others will be accepted.**
**Answers must be written clearly and neatly – otherwise marks may be lost.**

**1**   Add the time signature to each of these five examples.

10

Byrd

Schubert

Alexander L'Estrange

'Wanna walk with me?' from *Jazz Sessions*
© 2005 Faber Music Ltd
Extract reproduced by permission of Faber Music Ltd. All rights reserved.

**2**   Give the letter name of each of these notes. The first answer is given.

10

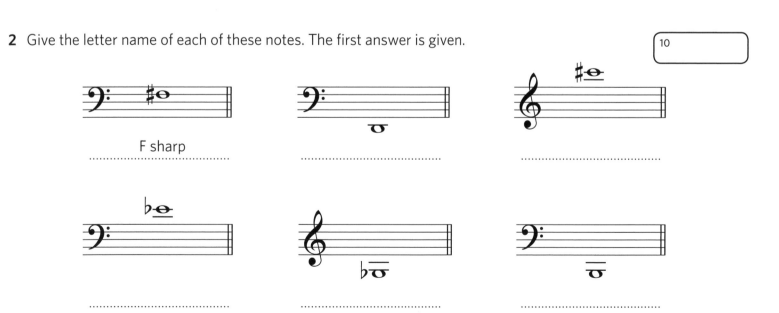

F sharp

.............................

.............................

.............................

.............................

.............................

.............................

**3** Describe each of these melodic intervals, giving the type and number (e.g. major 3rd, perfect 5th). The keys are named, and in each case the lower note is the key note.

[ 10 ]

A♭ major

B minor

G major

Type .......................

Type .......................

Type .......................

Number .......................

Number .......................

Number .......................

E♭ major

F♯ minor

Type .......................

Type .......................

Number .......................

Number .......................

**4** Add the correct clef and any necessary accidentals to each of these tonic triads. Do **not** use key signatures.

[ 10 ]

C♯ minor

B♭ major

A minor

G minor

E major

**5** Using semibreves (whole notes), write one octave of the scales named below.

[ 10 ]

A major, **ascending**, with key signature.

F **harmonic** minor, **descending**, without key signature but including any necessary accidentals.

**6** Add the correct rest(s) at the places marked ✳ in these two melodies to make each bar complete. [10]

Schumann

Wolf

**7** Rewrite this melody using notes and rests of **twice the value**. Remember to put in the new time signature at the place marked ✳, and remember to group (beam) the notes correctly. [10]

Mozart
etc.

etc.

**8** Tick one box for each term/sign, as shown in the first answer. [10]

| | means: | *triste* means: | | **Vivace** means: | |
|---|---|---|---|---|---|
| the end | ☐ | heavy | ☐ | lively, quick | ☐ |
| held back | ☐ | sad, sorrowful | ☐ | fairly quick | ☐ |
| double bar-line | ☐ | playful, merry | ☐ | slow | ☐ |
| repeat mark | ✔ | slow, stately | ☐ | at a medium speed | ☐ |

| **Tempo comodo** means: | | *subito* means: | | *poco* means: | |
|---|---|---|---|---|---|
| with some freedom of time | ☐ | simple, plain | ☐ | a little | ☐ |
| gradually getting slower | ☐ | sad | ☐ | in time | ☐ |
| at a comfortable speed | ☐ | sustained | ☐ | held back | ☐ |
| first time | ☐ | suddenly | ☐ | detached | ☐ |

**9** Look at this melody by Hofmann and then answer the questions below.

*Write your answer to question (b) on the stave below.*

(a) (i) The melody is in the key of F major. Give the number of
a bar that contains **all** the notes of the tonic triad in this key.   Bar ............

    (ii) Which other key has the same key signature as F major?   ....................................

    (iii) Name the degree of the scale (e.g. 4th, 5th) of the last
note of the melody. Remember that the key is F major.   ............

    (iv) Answer TRUE or FALSE to this statement:

       The melody begins on the third beat of the bar.   ...........................

    (v) Underline one of the following words that best describes how bar 3 should be played.

           *legato* (smoothly)   or   *staccato* (detached)

(b) Using the blank stave above question (a), write out the melody from the beginning of
bar 5 to the end of the music **an octave lower**, using the bass clef as shown.